G000144293

The Man With
Leprosy

Published edition © 2007 Lost Sheep Resources Pty Ltd.
Text and illustrations © 2007 Andrew McDonough

© 2007 Lost Sheep Resources Pty Ltd. Lost Sheep is a trademark of Lost Sheep Resources Pty Ltd.

All rights reserved. No part of this book may be reproduced in any form or by any means without prior permission from the publishers.

The Bible text is from The Bible for Today (Contemporary English Version) © American Bible Society 1991, 1995. Used by permission of the Bible Society in Australia Inc (1995), GPO Box 507, Canberra ACT 2601.

First printing July 2007
16 15 14 13 12 11 10 09 08 07   10 9 8 7 6 5 4 3 2 1

National Library of Australia
Cataloguing-in-Publication entry

    McDonough, Andrew (Andrew John).
    The man with leprosy.
    For primary school children.
    ISBN 9781921229107 (hbk.).
    1. Bible. N.T. Mark I, 40-45 - Juvenile literature. 2.
    Healing of the leper (Miracle) - Juvenile literature. 3.
    Bible stories, English - Juvenile literature. 4. Jesus
    Christ - Juvenile literature. 5. Picture books for
    children. I. Title. (Series : McDonough, Andrew (Andrew
    John) Lost sheep. Series 3 ; 11).
    226.3

Bandage washers: Jim and Robyn Nottingham
Cake decorator: Bronwyn Drew
This book should be read within thirty days of opening.

Designed and published by Lost Sheep

Lost Sheep
PO Box 3191
Unley SA 5061
Australia
info@lostsheep.com.au
lostsheep.com.au

Printed in China by Color Patch

The Man With Leprosy

Andrew McDonough

It's not much fun being sick.

A runny nose is bad, an earache is worse.

So, if you've ever been sick, you've got to feel sorry for the man with leprosy.

He had blotches on his belly.

He had aching arms and lumpy bumpy leprosy legs.

You would think that everyone would be kind to the man with leprosy, but no.

When he walked down the street, people would start to run away yelling, "Look out! Look out! A leper! A leper!"

His family wanted to hug him, but no one was allowed to touch a person with leprosy.

The man with leprosy thought, "Maybe God will help me." So he went to the temple, but the priest said, "No lepers allowed!"

The man with leprosy left the temple, left his family and limped out of town.

Jesus was strolling into town when he saw the man limping towards him on his lumpy bumpy leprosy legs. Jesus stopped. As the man came closer and closer, Jesus could see his aching arms and the blotches on his belly.

The man with leprosy knelt down in front of Jesus and cried and cried, "Help me, Jesus! Everybody runs away from me. I'm not allowed in the temple and I'm not allowed to hug my family. I know that if you want to, you can make me better."

Jesus' heart ached. He put his arm around the man with leprosy and hugged him. "I'd love to make you better," said Jesus.

And the leprosy vanished. Jesus and the man without leprosy jumped up and down and cheered, "Hooray! Hooray! Hooray!"

"Now listen!" whispered Jesus. "Do not tell anyone I healed you! Just tiptoe to the temple and show the priest you're better. Got that? Do not tell anyone!"

But the man without leprosy was so excited he ran into town shouting, "I'm healed! I'm healed! Jesus healed me! Jesus healed me!"

"Look!" he said to the priest. "Jesus healed my lumpy bumpy leprosy legs!"

"Well," said the priest, "you'd better walk those legs into the temple and thank God."

"Look!" he said to the people. "Jesus healed my blotchy belly!"

"Well," said the people, "that belly needs some cake."

"Look!" said the man to his family. "Jesus healed my aching arms!"

"Well," said his family, "you'd better stretch out those arms and give us a great big hug!"

The Back Page

The Man with Leprosy is based on the story Jesus told in Mark 1:40-44. In this story we see how Jesus felt about people who were sick and treated badly. We also get to see what he did to help them. This is a good way to encourage children to have the same attitude towards everyone who is sick, hurting or sad.

Before the Story

A good place to start is by asking,
"When you're sick or feeling sad, how do you like people to treat you?"
Tell them that this is a story about a person who was sick and sad, and about the people he met.

Read the Story

After the Story

You may like to ask,
"Why did people run away from the man with leprosy?
How did the man with leprosy feel when others didn't want to be around him?
How do you think Jesus felt when he saw the man walking towards him?"
Have a look through the book together to find the times when the man was happy.
"What does this teach us about the way Jesus would like us to treat people who are sick or feeling sad?"

God's blessing,
Andrew